The
ULTIMATE
GUIDEBOOK
FOR GETTING INTO
MEDICAL SCHOOL

Chad Rudnick, MD

To my best friend & wife
Ashley
Thank you for everything

Additional thanks to my sister, Meredith, and my
parents, Jerry and Michele, for all your help and support

Foreword

I was asked on numerous occasions while completing this book how I was able to find the time to author a book while completing my pediatric residency. Thanks to the new residency duty hours which began in July 2011, limiting residents to 80 hours and at least one day off per week, there was time to complete this project, albeit in small chunks here and there.

I always knew that I wanted to be a doctor, although professional baseball player was, and still is on my list of career choices. Knowing that the first step toward a career in medicine was to first attend college and earn a degree, I was ecstatic to be accepted into my top choice, the University of Florida, following my high school graduation.

Prior to beginning freshman year of college, students attended a freshman orientation where we were given the task of basically choosing the next four years of our lives all in a weekend with what seemed like absolutely zero guidance.

With a 500+ page course catalog and a smaller notebook we were tasked with planning out the next few semesters' worth of courses. I struggled, but with the help of friends who were a year ahead of me and already knew which electives were "the ones to take", I created a schedule. Later, with some tinkering, my schedule would satisfy all of the medical school requirements and enable me to focus enough time on each course to earn a high GPA, graduate *Cum Laude* (with honors), and earn acceptance to medical school following my senior year of college.

Aside from planning out a college course schedule, there is so much more information which is necessary to strengthen your candidacy for medical school, information which was not in any course catalog or freshman manual. After being asked by many over the years about what it really takes to get into medical school, I decided to write this book to put it straight to young adults who aspire to be a doctor.

- What does it really mean when medical school applications say something is recommended, but not required?
- What about all of the extracurricular activities, research experience, and leadership roles?
- What is the true importance of the Medical College Admissions Test (MCAT)?
- Do I need a high GPA?
- How do you impress on your interview?
- How do you know which schools to apply?
- What about everything else?

I hope that this book will serve as a guide to assist you in preparing and planning your high school and college experiences, to ultimately improve your application and candidacy for medical school and becoming a medical student.

Table of Contents

Pre-Rounds

Have a plan and prepare yourself!

The very hands that hold this book, your hands, could be the ones that deliver a mother's first child, perform life saving surgery, or find the cure for cancer. Your future holds infinite power and you are taking the first step on the road to becoming a doctor.

There is no sugar coating, no hiding of the truth, becoming a doctor takes hard work and dedication. There are many nights spent staring at open textbooks with tired eyes, just praying that you will get through the following day's exam. Days turn into nights, and seem to combine into one long study marathon at the end of which you sometimes feel as if you know less than at the start of the race. For all of the long hours, extra help sessions, and countless slices of late night fuel (i.e. pizza and coffee) there is absolutely no way I would go back and change my dream of becoming a doctor.

As a medical student, typically in the third year, you begin to see patients on a daily basis. You are often able to follow the same patient or patients each day from the time they are admitted to the hospital until the time they are able to be sent home safely.

Seeing patients each day, during a process known as rounds, the team of medical students, resident physicians, and attending (head) physician will examine patients and together with the patient and often their family, discuss their condition and treatment plan. In order for the entire team of students and physicians to be prepared on rounds, we must complete our "pre-rounds." This is where each patient is spoken with, examined, and had their previous day or overnight vital signs (blood pressure, heart rate, respiratory rate, etc.) reviewed along with any new laboratory or diagnostic tests that were performed the previous day.

Pre-rounds are an essential part of caring for your patients with preparedness the key to making morning rounds with the attending smooth, and provide the best care for your patients. In order to earn an acceptance into medical school, students must pre-round. This is best beginning in high school and continuing until the first day of medical school, when your "rounds" can start.

In the year 2011, there were nearly 44,000 applicants to medical schools in the United States. Of the nearly 44,000 students who applied, 19,230 were accepted into a medical school program in the United States. You do not need to know calculus to understand that earning an acceptance into medical school is no easy task. Having a plan and starting your medical school pre-rounds early will help you earn acceptance into, in my opinion, the greatest career in the world.

1. How Will I Learn All Of The Information?

The amount of medical material that you must learn and synthesize into the various compartments in your brain is, for lack of a better term, massive. This begins, to some extent, with courses in high school and quickly increases in college and medical school.

Fortunately, medical schools do not expect their applicants to have vast amounts or any amount of medical knowledge for that matter before starting medical school. The purpose for all of the entrance exams, undergraduate grades, etc, is to determine which students have the capacity to handle the rigors of a medical school curriculum as well as the personality to be successful as a physician, hence the personal statement and interview (more on this later).

A mentor of mine gave me an analogy to how physicians are seemingly able to remember nearly every fact about their respective specialty and recall large amounts of esoteric material. When we begin our careers in medicine, as medical students, our knowledge can be pictured as an empty net with huge holes throughout.

As you begin to learn and continuing throughout most of your career, all the information/facts you are taught will fall toward your net. With the large holes that are undoubtedly present at the beginning of your career, it is expected that most of the information will fall through and not be remembered. However, as information is presented which has a relation to another area which you were already familiar with, a connection will be formed in your net. Over time, as more information is presented and learned, many of the holes and space in your net will be filled in. While it is impossible to learn everything there is to know about medicine, your "net" will become more and more dense, allowing less and less information to pass through, especially when you matriculate through medical school, residency, and beyond.

Physicians are never finished learning, there is always more to read about the diseases and treatments which affect our patients. While even the most experienced and well read physician will have a dense net with small holes, they still will have holes in their net, meaning that even a great clinician needs to continue to read and learn in order to become as knowledgeable as possible so that they can better serve their patients.

I. Elementary Years

Start with ABC's, not $a^2+b^2 = c^2$

Author Robert Fulghum's book, "All I Really Need To Know I Learned In Kindergarten" has its place in many careers, including medicine. However, children with dreams of becoming young prominent physicians still need their to start with the ABC's, not the Pythagorean theorem.

There are many occasions where parents have asked whether or not their child should be tested for a gifted program when they are in pre-school or kindergarten. While some children undoubtedly will benefit from early stimulation via a gifted program, all children should be encouraged to explore, play, and learn at a pace expected of their age group.

Enrolling in or missing out on an elementary gifted program is probably unlikely to affect the ultimate career and learning potential of a child. The more important factors that determine a child's success are ensuring that they are encouraged to read, learn, and be exposed to education from infancy on.

I can still remember the PA system in my elementary school classroom calling my name through the speaker, something that for a 6-year old is both exciting, because your name is seemingly being summoned from the heavens, and scary, because in the back of your mind you wonder if you got into big trouble without even knowing what you did. I walked down to the office, via the buddy system of course, and was sat in a chair in our assistant principal's office. At least, I believe she was the assistant principal (all I knew is she was someone would scold you for not behaving appropriately in the lunch room). Nevertheless, she sat across from me with my light up sneakers, messy hair, and I'm sure a once clean t-shirt that was probably stained with the remnants of recess and lunch.

Prepared for my gifted exam, I was ready to discuss real adult issues, ready for anything that she could ask.

"Chad, why do we take baths?"

Could this really be the question that I was being tested on in order to start the following year in the gifted classroom? How much more simple could it be?

Then the moment of truth happened, as simple as the question may be, formulating more than a few uh's and um's proved to be quite the challenge. I managed a response similar to the effect of, "We need them because we get dirty."

Phew, that was easy, now bring on the study of the Franco-Prussian war and the analysis of Adam Smith's thoughts on economics. The rest of the questioning probably went like the first response, typical 6 year old answers, but none that I can remember.

Day two of testing went differently, this time in the media center, where I once learned the ancient art of using a library catalog system. The examiner, a man wearing glasses sat across from me at a small table, the only other detail about him which I recall was the stopwatch he held in his hand. I remember thinking that I would definitely ace this portion of the testing. A physical fitness test, please, watch me run circles around the other gifted six-year olds.

The only time the stopwatch came out and the only part of the exam I remember was trying to put together the body of a horse with oddly shaped puzzle pieces. Thinking that this would be a breeze for me, after all, my dad is a horse veterinarian and I grew up riding horses nearly my whole life.

As the timer continued to tick on, I had the horse put together, sort of. The horse was together, but it looked odd, head, tail and legs where in the right place, but I still had one piece left and nowhere to place it. Thinking it was a trick puzzle, I simply said, "Done!" The examiner then pointed to my clenched right fist and spoke, "What about that one?"

It was several months later that I found out that I would not be joining the gifted program as a second grader, not such a huge blow, as none of my friends were in the program either.

Enrollment in the gifted program as a six year old does not dictate the rest of your life. The early process by which parents and teachers encourage reading, writing, and free play helps to stimulate the minds of young children to explore, ask questions, and develop a passion for lifelong learning.

Young and old, current and future physicians all started with the ABC's, the basics. The majority of my colleagues and I were not in the gifted program in elementary or middle school.

We were not born knowing the branches of arteries coming off the aorta or how to properly examine and treat a child with asthma. We were given the tools to succeed and through studying and hard work, were accepted to study and practice the art of medicine.

II. Looking Back To Early School Days

Arguably some of the most awkward and difficult times in a child's life, grades six through eight are associated with more than algebra, lockers, and switching classrooms every period.

Rarely does a child have a completely unflustered time adjusting to the changes their bodies go through during puberty. Having far from smooth skin and seeing other, further developed classmates can be a difficult adjustment for an adolescent.

While this is occurring, I often hear from concerned parents that their child's grades are suffering and they are worried that their son or daughter will not be able to enroll in honors classes in high school.

No child has been unable to become a doctor because they earned a 'B' in seventh grade science class. However, my colleagues and I have seen bright young children fall short of their potential because of decisions that are made during these years.

Even though the grades you earn in middle school are unlikely to affect what medical school you ultimately attend, study skills and the commitment to learning that starts during these years will help to ease the transition to more difficult courses and work load in the years ahead.

Enrolling in honors courses during the middle school years are an excellent way to have initial exposure to curriculum that moves at a faster pace. This imposes a higher level of responsibility in an adolescent to study more effectively in order to continue earning high grades. Additionally, honors courses completed during middle school also help guide teachers in recommending the student for honors and advanced placement (AP) courses once they matriculate into high school.

Leaving the confines of elementary school, where as a fifth grader standing around five feet two inches tall, towering over smaller first and second graders, I started my first week of sixth grade, middle school.

Just having returned from a summer camp in upstate New York, I was still in "summer mode", where my days were spent meeting for morning announcements at the flag pole, followed by breakfast, and then an entire day's worth of sports and activities. Rarely having to change out of my basketball shorts and a t-shirt, it was a 12-year-old's dream summer.

When sixth grade started that year, I was enrolled in all honors classes, except for PE and Home Economics, which I don't think had an honors section. I had straight A's almost every quarter during elementary school, except when handwriting counted as a separate grade. My penmanship was terrible, and to this day probably isn't much better, but thankfully our electronic medical record system has enabled me to leave my poor handwriting to thank-you notes and filling out school physicals for my patients. Everything that middle school was going to represent sounded pretty good in my book.

I don't remember what I wore to school the first day, but I'm sure I could go through an old photo album at my parents house which probably captured the smile on the face of my overweight frame with hair spray and mousse filled hair. If only there was social media back in the middle to late 1990s, the picture would probably be a lot more accessible to me and the rest of my Facebook friends.

My sixth grade math honors math class, filled with students from other elementary schools in the area, was in a portable classroom which stood on cinder blocks in the 6B block of portables that represented the majority of my classrooms. The portables were set up in two rows with a large walkway in between, labeled 6A through 6G. The letter represented which 'team' of teachers you would have for the year. Not all of the letters were created equal as I would find out early in the year; the 'G' in 6G was for the gifted classes.

There was not much difference whether you were in the honors course or the honors-G. We would all still learn at the same accelerated pace, which I would quickly learn was a little more than I was prepared for.

On the first day of school, our math teacher, Mrs. A, told us that we would all take a test the following day to determine our baseline mathematics knowledge and also to make sure that we were in the correct course for our abilities. The next day as I sat at my desk with my freshly sharpened #2 pencil, I was handed a scantron and a test booklet. It was on question number three that everything started to unravel, the questions seemed to be written in hieroglyphics.

I didn't remember learning any of this material in fourth or fifth grade math. Thankfully, I finished the test and handed in my scantron, just happy to be done with the exam and ready for lunch. A few days later I remember being pulled to the side as I handed in a homework assignment at the teacher's desk and was told that my score was low on the math exam and Mrs. A was concerned that I might not be able to handle the material and the pace at which we would be moving throughout the year.

Up until that point, my penmanship may not have been up to par with other students, but never was I told that I could not keep up in math. I loved math and told Mrs. A that I could handle it and would be able to keep up. Eight weeks later, the A on my report card showed her that I was able to handle honors mathematics. As I reflect on it now, Mrs. A probably did me a huge favor by telling me that my initial test score was low, as it pushed me to do my homework and extra practice problems so that I was able to understand the material for each test.

2.   Volunteering

Along with scholastic material and staying active through sports and exercise, this is an excellent time for aspiring doctors and all children to be exposed to volunteer work. Whether you are volunteering to collect toys for underprivileged children or helping to clean up your local park, the realization that some free time needs to be spent helping your community and others will help to strengthen your candidacy for college, medical school, and residency.

Volunteer work that is done when you are an early teenager has no bearing on what residency program (the step after medical school) you will train with. And in case you were wondering, volunteering does not always have to be done in a hospital.

One of the best ways to encourage and keep someone wanting to volunteer is to have them volunteer doing or helping others do things that they also love. For example, if someone loves sports and being outside, then consider volunteering at the Special Olympics.

Taking young athletes around to their events is a great way to give back to the community and learn that while some children and adults may look different on the outside, everyone can participate and compete in activities and sports which make them happy.

Always active in my youth group growing up, I had the opportunity to volunteer at the Special Olympics in South Florida. Along with another friend from my youth group, I was assigned to one of the young athletes. We were given a copy of his competition schedule and would walk with him to his events and cheer him on as he would compete. I still remember how fast he was, winning all of his track events, and how after each race he would hug every one of his competitors, the award presenters and of course, my friend and me.

During my fourth year of medical school, working at the sports medicine clinic, I found myself examining an adult athlete who competes in the Special Olympics. I would later find out that they once held a United States record in a track & field event. Now, as a pediatric resident, I am able to work with children with disabilities every day. Whether seeing them for their annual well-child checkup or treating them when they are feeling ill, I feel privileged to be a small part of their lives.

Helping others through volunteer work as a young adult teaches us to value the things we have as well as time management skills. The latter enabling you to keep grades strong as volunteering continues in high school, college, medical school, and beyond.

Volunteer activities should be treated like a job, taking responsibility for the tasks that you are assigned to and always being on time. It is important to contact your boss or in this case, volunteer coordinator if you are unable to make it to a volunteer activity that you previously signed up for. Volunteer hours and experiences collected during high school and college will also help strengthen applications for college and medical school, respectively.

How to be a star volunteer?

- ✓ Always be on time!
- ✓ Check in with the leader of the volunteers each day.
- ✓ Introduce yourself to other staff members and volunteers.
- ✓ Shake hands with people you meet!
- ✓ If your job is finished, ask how you can help someone else with their task.
- ✓ Be polite to everyone!

Now more than ever, college institutions are looking for well rounded students whom they believe will not only attend their university to pay tuition and receive an education, but also give back to the community through their continued efforts in extracurricular and volunteer activities. Volunteering should start while in middle school and continue during high school, college, and beyond.

How do you get involved in volunteering?

- ✓ Start by going online and searching for volunteer projects in your community.
- ✓ Ask your teachers, religious institutions, or local hospital if there are any volunteer projects coming up that you can participate in.

A few projects available in my community:

- ✓ Neighborhood park or beach cleanup
- ✓ Serving food at a homeless shelter
- ✓ Working with the 4-H club (www.4-H.org)
- ✓ Volunteering at a local animal shelter/humane society
- ✓ Collecting toys for underprivileged children
- ✓ Spending time with the elderly at a nursing home
- ✓ Bringing toys and games to children who are in the hospital

III. High School

I have asked hundreds of high school students what they want to be when they grow up. The vast majority of answers are simple shoulder shrugs with barely audible mumblings resembling "I don't know."

As you enter high school, you should start to prepare your game plan for how you will eventually be accepted into medical school and become a doctor. The good news is that you do not need to know what kind of doctor you want be as a ninth or tenth grader. In fact, many medical students don't know what kind of doctor they want to be once they enter medical school.

There are a significant number of medical school students who made the commitment to pursue a career in medicine once they were already finished with high school. However, the road toward becoming a doctor can certainly be less bumpy and roundabout if learning, extracurricular activities, and volunteering are taken seriously during high school.

Prepare yourself by studying and asking for help early-on in subjects that you struggle with. This will help to inflate one of the most important parts of your college application: high school grade point average (GPA).

The answer from every college institution is that GPA is not the only thing that a school looks at when they assess your application. While that is undoubtedly true, the fact of the matter is, the road to becoming a doctor is much more difficult with a 3.0 GPA than it is with a perfect 4.0 GPA.

It is tough to set yourself apart from hundreds of thousands of high school students who are applying to colleges and universities across the nation every year. Since most universities do not conduct interviews for college freshman enrollment, your accolades and accomplishments need to jump off the page to the admissions committee.

Where your application can differ from other high school students:

- GPA and standardized test scores (SAT, ACT)
- Academic awards, honor society, etc.
- Volunteer work
- Work experience
- Extracurricular activities
- Varsity and junior varsity athletics
- Leadership roles
- Essays

3. Honors and Advanced Placement (AP) Classes

High school students who aspire be a physician should enroll in honors and advanced placement courses starting early in high school. Learning at a faster pace, these courses help to teach study skills as well as inflate your HPA (honors point average) to help your transcript and class rank improve. Additionally, AP classes, those which are taught and tested at a higher level than an honors course, offer the opportunity to earn college credit by passing a comprehensive exam at the end of the year.

I was enrolled in nearly all honors and a few advanced placement courses throughout high school and was able to earn mostly A's in my courses. The honors classes required me to study more than I probably would have needed to in order to earn an A in the regular section of a particular course. Having multiple honors classes each semester forced me to manage my time wisely while at home, which in turn helped to mold me into the person I am today.

Additionally, your success in advanced placement courses will show college admission committees that you are able to handle the rigors of a college course which eases their minds about accepting you into their institution. I highly recommend that high school students push themselves by enrolling in honors and advanced placement courses. The work that you put in during high school will pay off significantly when it comes time to apply to college.

Students do not need to be in all honors or AP classes during high school. Several courses, such as electives, will not have an honors or AP section. I encourage students to enroll in advanced placement courses in the subjects which they feel they are the strongest. So, if you are terrible at remembering facts in history and don't know what year the War of 1812 took place, then it is advisable for you to not enroll in AP United States history.

4. Dual Enrollment

To those with the opportunity, another benefit to your transcript and college application is to enroll in a dual-enrollment course during high school. Dual enrollment allows the high school student to take a particular course at a college or university in lieu of having that period in high school. Like standard AP classes, dual enrollment helps to set your application apart from other students who may not have enrolled nor had success in honors and AP courses. Set an appointment and talk to your high school guidance counselor about the necessary forms and qualifications needed for you to enroll in a course at a local college during the school year or during your summer break.

While it may seem ridiculous to actually want to take a college course during your summer break, remember that medicine is a commitment and the road to an M.D. degree starts with your acceptance into a strong undergraduate college or university.

Taking courses at a local college may be difficult and is probably unnecessary during your freshman year of high school, but should be considered following your sophomore and especially junior year of high school.

Students should strive to complete their dual-enrollment college level courses prior to the beginning of their senior year. This allows your transcript to reflect your successes in college level courses prior to applying to college. Remember that most high school students are accepted into college by the late fall or early spring of their senior year. Thus, dual-enrollment courses, which are started in the spring of your senior year, will not do much for your college application. Like advanced placement courses, dual enrollment courses also demonstrate to college and university admission committee members that you are likely able to handle the rigors of a college semester.

5. Standardized Tests

A sound on Sunday morning that nobody wants to hear is the incessant beeping of an alarm clock. For several months, a 7:00am wake up every Sunday morning was what I had to struggle with. You see, few things are more displeasing to a high school student than having to attend an SAT or ACT prep course on a weekend morning while their friends are at the beach.

There is no hiding the fact that performance on the SAT has a large bearing on your application for college. There are probably a few successful doctors who did not do well on their SAT exams. However, in order to be accepted to a top college or university and eventually your first choice for medical school, the higher your score, the better. Your goal should be to earn a perfect score on the SAT or ACT.

Early Saturday morning, without any additional SAT preparation, I arrived at the SAT exam with a stomach full from a complete breakfast, several sharpened #2 pencils in my pocket, and my driver's license in my hand. I was seated in a classroom unknown to me, ready to take my next step toward my goal of becoming a doctor.

I felt fairly confident after the mathematics portion of the examination; however, reading comprehension was slightly more of a guessing game.

I remember thinking to myself while reading one of the questions that accompanied a reading passage: "How am I supposed to know what the author was thinking?"

"How did the SAT question writers know what the author was thinking, did they ask them?"

"If the author was really thinking or implying something, why didn't they just write that instead of beating around the bush for seven paragraphs?"

I remember the feeling in my then empty stomach when I called the SAT results phone number to receive my score a few weeks early over the phone, now an essentially obsolete practice thanks to early reporting via the web. The numbers were read by the automated voice separately, and while setting up a simple arithmetic equation on my scrap piece of paper, added the two numbers, but did not trust the result. So I went to my desk drawer and returned with a calculator that confirmed that I was strong in math, while reading comprehension was less my forte.

The result of my first attempt at the SAT, while above the national average, was a rude awakening for me. I needed to put in much more time and effort in order to bring my score up to a result that I would be confident would help my application for college.

Additionally, being a high school student in the state of Florida in 2003, a SAT score of 1270 (we did not have a writing section in 2003) or higher along with a minimum 3.5 GPA would earn you a Bright Futures scholarship, where 100% of college tuition would be paid for by the state.

Putting in extra study hours, one to two times per week after school as well as every Sunday morning for a few months, I managed to raise my score above the magic Bright Futures scholarship threshold and earn a full scholarship to my top choice, the University of Florida. Go Gators!

Nearly every year the average SAT score is increasing for the incoming freshman classes to top-tier universities. In order to earn an acceptance into a top-tier college or university, you must perform well on your SAT, ACT, or both, along with a strong GPA, essays, and application.

While your top choices for college may be a result of wanting to stay close to home or wanting to attend a small, less well-known institution, your goal should be to attend the best college possible.

Finding the best college possible:

- ✓ Set up a meeting with your high school guidance counselor at the beginning of your junior year to discuss the college application process.
- ✓ Read online the rankings of the top colleges and universities such as those ranked every year by U.S. News.
- ✓ Make a list of schools that you are interested in and read their website information for prospective students.
- ✓ Narrow down your list and visit as many of the college campuses as you can prior to submitting your college applications to determine which one is the best fit for you.

Strive to earn an education from a college or university with a long track record of educating some of the best and brightest students. You should strongly consider attending a college or university that graduates a number of students who attend medical schools around the country every year. Remember that if you attend a small college that has never had a student accepted into medical school, it is making it that much more difficult on yourself to achieve your dream of becoming a physician.

- ✓ Take the initiative early, purchase an SAT prep book, and read study tips in order to do well on the exam.
- ✓ Take practice tests and work through the solutions in order to learn the concepts that are being tested.
- ✓ Do not wait to ask for help preparing for the SATs, regardless of how your friends are preparing for the exam; the only thing that is important is how well you are prepared on the day of the exam.

- ✓ Ask your school guidance counselor if there is a SAT preparation course offered at your school, sign up for a prep course in your community, or purchase access through a prep course online.
- ✓ Before paying for any extra help, you must research the company offering the course and read reviews. Look for information from websites other than the company's and from other students using the prep course in previous years to determine if they will help you achieve your goal score.

6. Extracurricular Activities

Guidance counselors and university admissions board committee members from every school across the country will tell you that extracurricular activities will help to strengthen your application for college. Even with the goal of medical school and becoming a physician in your sights, your extracurricular activities do not need to only involve the medical profession. Whether your extracurricular activities have you as the president of your high school theatre troupe or as a member of the varsity wrestling team, what is most important is finding something you like doing and performing to the best of your ability.

I grew up always playing sports with my brothers and sister. My brothers, David and Eric, and I probably spent what would add up to months outside playing catch or one-on-one basketball in the driveway. Proudly, I have never lost in a game of one-on-one to either of my brothers, even to this very day.

I was a little league baseball player for most of my childhood and then switched my focus to basketball as I got older. Before entering high school, I considered trying out for the freshman basketball team, however at five feet six inches tall as a freshman who could not jump very high, I realized that my only chances in the NBA would likely be as a team president or owner.

David, three years older than me, had joined the wrestling team at our high school and became extremely successful, so naturally, I had to join the wrestling team with him my freshman year, his senior year. He pushed me to work hard and drill my takedowns and escapes (wrestling terms) over and over until they literally were second nature and merely muscle memory.

With the score tied after three periods of wrestling, I was fatigued; muscles burning from lactic acid build up. But the match wasn't over yet; a sudden death overtime period would decide whether I would represent the varsity wrestling team at 125 lbs or whether I would spend time on the junior varsity squad. I have never wanted to be second fiddle, always wanting to excel at anything that I did, the overtime period began and was over in just a few seconds.

My opponent attempted to take me to the mat in a headlock, and in the moment when he would score the takedown, two points, and the victory, I managed to continue the headlock and use his momentum to re-roll him. Two points and the win, for me, a freshman member of the varsity wrestling team. Four years and 101 victories later, I finished my high school wrestling career.

While I had success during my high school wrestling career, my greatest accomplishment, thanks in large part to my coach and parents, was the dedication, lessons, and teamwork that I learned during those four memorable years.

Dedication to an extremely difficult sport meant staying in shape both during the wrestling season as well as during the off season in order to lose and maintain my weight in a healthy manner. I also had to dedicate countless hours to practicing takedowns, escapes, and pinning combinations. I quickly learned there was no better feeling for me then to have my hand raised, often exhausted, but nevertheless victorious over my opponent following a difficult wrestling match.

Along with the spoils of victory comes the agony of defeat for a wrestler. When you are out matched by an opponent, while having your shoulders pinned to the mat despite your greatest efforts, one learns to deal with but never accept defeat.

Losing a match was an awful feeling and served as fuel to my desire to be the best and continue to work hard in order to not be on the losing end of a wrestling match.

I used this mindset to push myself to never settle for anything lower than an A which enabled me to finish near the top of my class in high school and graduate with honors in college.

While a wrestling match is one-on-one, you versus your opponent, there is a tremendous amount of teamwork that occurs behind the scenes of the match. To learn and become a great wrestler, it takes great coaches and teammates to help push you to your limits and help you achieve your greatest potential in the sport. I would not have been as successful during my wrestling career had it not been for my great coach and teammates who would push me when I felt like I did not want to continue, wanted to give up.

Since retiring from wrestling, my fellow residents along with our attending physicians and nursing staff have become a part of my new team. Medicine is best practiced as a team, with ideas, lists of a differential diagnosis, along with treatment plans discussed and carried out amongst our group of physicians and nurses. Together with the patient, or in many cases, the patient's family, the medical team can approach a set of symptoms, diagnose and correctly treat the patient, and provide an action plan which can help to limit the reoccurrence or worsening of the illness.

It is impossible to learn about everything in medicine and there will be countless times when you will need to approach your colleagues and rely on them for help with your patients. The values that I learned at a young age in order to be a contributing member to a team has helped me to become a better doctor and will continue to help me provide the best care for my patients and their families for decades to come.

7. Résumé

When in doubt, write it down!

Nearly every activity, event, or experience that you are a part of in high school should be written down so that when it comes time to apply to college, those experiences all can be recalled and entered into the correct section of the application. A great tip that I tell to high school students is to create a spreadsheet on their computer with the name and date of the activity, number of hours spent, and a contact person who could verify their attendance.

Also, include a short 2 to 4 sentence description of what you did and what you may have learned. Having an ongoing list available on your computer will help to make the experience of creating and updating your resume for college and medical school less problematic.

A résumé is essentially the paper version to the question, "Tell me about yourself?" While all résumés look a little different, your résumé should have key features and a theme which is present throughout the document.

As you move forward through high school, college, and medical school, new sections will be added and others removed.

Note that résumé is most often called curriculum vitae (CV) in the medical profession.

Your basic college level résumé should include the following sections:

- Name, address, e-mail, phone number
- Education
- Honors and awards
- Employment/work experience
- Extracurricular activities
- Volunteer experience

Additional sections that may be included in your medical school résumé include:

- Publications (scientific & non-scientific)
- Research in progress
- Professional society memberships
- Professional activities
- Presentations
- Professional meetings attended
- Hobbies

Not all of the sections listed above will be in every student's résumé and the list above is not all-inclusive. It is important to have your résumé reviewed by your school's guidance counselor, college advisor, or physician-mentor prior to submission to ensure that all necessary elements are included. Your résumé should be continually updated throughout your career, with older, less important entries removed as newer accolades and accomplishments are added. Unless there were awards or accomplishments achieved during high school that are truly outstanding, your high school accomplishments should not be a part of your medical school application/résumé.

A basic outline of a résumé, where a list of your education, awards, etc. is added to the right of the each date, and additional sections can be added as you complete them during your schooling. Since this is a basic format of a résumé, students are free to change the layout, font, add or remove sections, but should remember that one of the keys to having a successful résumé is the ease of reading for any person who is reviewing your résumé.

A physician or teacher who is reviewing your accomplishments either to give you advice or to prepare a letter of recommendation should be able to quickly see each part of your résumé which can only be accomplished if it is not cluttered and is in an easy to read format such as what is listed below.

Passport sized
professional picture

Name

Address

Phone number

E-mail Address

EDUCATION
2003-Present

AWARDS
2006-Present
2005-Present
2005-Present
2005
2003-Present

EMPLOYMENT
2004-Present
2000-03

Résumé tips:

- ✓ Think clean and professional
- ✓ Use specialty résumé paper when printing your résumé for a more formal look
- ✓ Email your résumé as a .pdf file to prevent reading and formatting errors
- ✓ Edit your résumé to include your most relevant achievements and avoid making it a novel.
- ✓ Try to keep it at 1 page and never more than 2 pages in length.
- ✓ Make sure your contact information is up to date.
- ✓ Have an email address which is professional, such as YourName@example.com

IV. The College Years

While it's not like in the movies, college years are one of the great experiences of one's life. In a non-scientific poll that I conducted with medical students and residents, the response to the question of would you like to go back to college, is almost always a resounding "Yes!"

You will also be hard pressed to find a medical student or resident physician who says that they had as much fun as possible during their college career. This is likely due to the fact that they missed out on at least a few parties or events because they had to study, complete assignments, or prepare for an exam. I was no exception to this. While I certainly had an amazing college experience at the University of Florida, there were more than a few parties and events that I had to pass up because studying for my courses was more important.

You will need to realize that many of your friends who do not have aspirations to become a doctor may have easier courses than you do during certain semesters. It may seem at times that everyone else is having all the fun and you are stuck in the library for 12 hours a day studying so you can earn an A in your organic chemistry course. While this will undoubtedly be true at some point, remember to always keep your eyes on the prize, becoming a doctor.

As important as it is to study and complete assignments and homework, you must choose the courses that you take wisely. It is probably unwise to try and take physics, biology, general chemistry, and calculus all in the same semester. While I am sure that it has been done by many people, having a plan and setting your sights on a career as a doctor early (before college starts) can help you to plan out your course load each semester so that you can devote the necessary time to each course in order to earn an A.

Balance your core medical school required courses (no more than 3 per semester) with less intense electives which also satisfy requirements for your university and also your major. This will also allow you time to study and enjoy your life as a young adult in what promises to be some of the greatest experiences of your life.

Basic course requirements for most medical schools are as follows:

- ✓ Biology – one year (two semesters) along with an accompanying laboratory course.
- ✓ Chemistry – two years (four semesters), along with an accompanying laboratory course. This typically consists of two semesters of general chemistry and two semesters of organic chemistry.
- ✓ Biochemistry – one semester.
- ✓ Physics – one year (two semesters), often with a laboratory course.
- ✓ Mathematics – one year (two semesters) of high level mathematics, usually calculus or an equivalent.

✓ Writing – at least one year (two semesters) of a course which satisfies a college level writing requirement.

Additional courses may be required and individual school requirements should be viewed several semesters in advance so that all required medical school courses are complete in order for your medical school application to be processed on time. There are also a few courses which my fellow classmates or I had completed during college which can help immensely during medical school. Consider these courses if there is room in your schedule, as they look good to an admissions committee and will help you during your first two years of medical school:

✓ Anatomy
✓ Physiology
✓ Pathophysiology
✓ Microbiology
✓ Introduction to Neuroscience
✓ Psychology

8. MCAT – Medical College Admissions Test

If there is one area that is most crucial, most utterly important for acceptance to a top tier medical school (or any medical school for that matter), it's the MCAT. The MCAT is now a 5 ½ hour computer-based exam testing physical science, biological science, verbal reasoning, and writing skills. The biological science, verbal reasoning, and physical science sections are each scored scale from 1 to 15, with a perfect score equaling 45.

For the first time in my career, I can say that *back in my day*, I took the MCAT with a pencil, scantron, and giant test booklet filled with the questions that would essentially determine one's candidacy for medical school.

The Association of American Medical Colleges (AAMC) reported the average score in 2011 for students in the United States who completed the MCAT was between 26.0 and 30.1. Additionally, the average MCAT score for students who entered medical school in 2011 according to the AAMC was 31.1.

The question that is always asked by undergraduate college students is what score they need to get into medical school. The truth is, there no magic number that guarantees acceptance. Every medical school applicant has heard stories or myths of a 4.0 college student who scored a 42 on their MCAT but didn't get into medical school. My response to that myth is to ask the question, "Are they really telling the truth?" If so, what on their application stands out so blatantly poor that they would not be granted admission to medical school?

The reality is that you do need to score highly on the MCAT if you want your application to appear strong enough on paper so that you will be invited to an interview for medical school admission. We will discuss more on interviews later.

When I was in college, there was another rumor that circulated amongst the pre-medical students on campus that an MCAT score of 30 would be a "magic" number to be invited to a least a few interviews. While many would subscribe to this rumor, it really is not true. A score of 30 has become much more commonplace at competitive medical schools and a score above 30, along with a strong application, letters of recommendation, and personal statement are now the norm.

Admissions directors typically say that the MCAT score is not the sole reason why students are invited or rejected for an interview. Truth be told, there still is a cutoff point where schools typically will not invite students to interview if their scores fall below an arbitrary mark. Unfortunately, no one will admit what that number is, but searching online for average class MCAT scores for the schools you are interested in applying will give you the idea of what caliber of students are typically accepted to a particular school.

In addition to the MCAT score, all parts of the medical school application should be considered supremely important. Having an outstanding application, complete with a high GPA, great letters of recommendation, extracurricular activities, a phenomenal personal statement, leadership experience, research experience, and publications can together make up for an MCAT score which may not be as high as you would like.

There is no sure combination of MCAT score, grades, extracurricular activities, research, etc. that will guarantee your admission into medical school. Every student's application is viewed in its entirety, assuming they meet minimum GPA and MCAT requirements. Excelling, not just getting by with mediocrity, at each of the parts of the application mentioned above should ensure that you are invited to interview at several programs across the country.

9. MCAT After The Year 2015

Starting in the year 2015, the writing portion of the MCAT will be removed from the exam. With the elimination of the writing portion of the exam, there will be two new sections added to the test: Psychological, Social, and Biological Foundations of Behavior as well as Critical Analysis and Reasoning Skills. Along with the new changes set to begin in 2015 and last until at least 2030, the exam will last around 6 hours and 30 minutes and is expected to be scored similar to the current exam, with scores of 1 to 15 per section, now with a total of 4 multiple choice sections, the score will likely be out of 60, rather than the current 45.

The Psychological, Social, and Biological Foundations of Behavior will focus on the information that is taught in undergraduate level courses in psychology, sociology, and biology. This change, per the AAMC will "test examinees' knowledge and use of concepts in psychology, sociology, and biology that provide a solid foundation for learning in medical school about the behavioral and socio-cultural determinants of health."

The Critical Analysis and Reasoning Skills section essentially will replace the current Verbal Reasoning portion of the exam. Currently, the Verbal Reasoning section of the exam is based on 7 passages consisting of topics ranging from humanities, social sciences, and natural sciences with five to seven questions per passage.

The Critical Analysis and Reasoning Skills section will also have examinees analyze passages from a range of behavioral and social sciences and humanities, as well as possible passages dealing with ethics, philosophy, and population health. This section of the exam will not require any specific knowledge about the subjects of the passage, as all of the needed information will appear in the passages. It will instead test a student's ability to read and synthesize the information in order to answer the questions, which sounds eerily similar to the dreaded reading comprehension portion of the SAT.

10. MCAT Preparation

It is difficult but not impossible to prepare for the MCAT exam by yourself. This exam is unlike the SAT which many students are able to score high on without much extra help or practice. The MCAT is as much an exam where you must learn about how to take the exam as it is the material which is being tested. Whether you choose to use a review/study book or to take a live or online review course, I always recommend students to sign up for some type of review course. Prior to doing so, take a practice section or exam available online to see what areas you are deficient in to learn your strengths and weaknesses when it comes to preparing for the test.

Bleary-eyed at 9:00 on a Sunday morning, the campus was desolate, after all, there are very few college students on campus, let alone awake at 9:00 on a Sunday morning. Nevertheless, it was the first session of my MCAT review course. I was enrolled in a live review course which met once per week for around six months before my exam.

After taking attendance, the MCAT review teacher, a medical student at the University of Florida College of Medicine asked us to fill out a short questionnaire for the MCAT review company. These would be placed into our files so that all of the MCAT teachers would be aware of our strengths and weaknesses to provide help should we attend a different section of the review course. One of the questions asked simply, "What is your goal MCAT score?"

I wrote down my number, 37, which seemed like a very respectable score in my mind. After our teacher collected the surveys from us, he quickly looked through them and stated, "You are all wrong."

He questioned us as to why no one wrote 45 as their goal score. Why had we all set a goal that was less than perfect? We were already selling ourselves short and we hadn't even started reviewing for the MCAT. In retrospect, he was absolutely correct to tell us that we were wrong to shortchange ourselves and strive for a goal score that was less than perfect.

Every question on the MCAT has an answer (whether you believe it or not) and there is no reason why everyone who takes the exam can't potentially score perfect. This should be your goal for everything you wish to achieve in medicine from this point forward. Whether the SAT, ACT, MCAT, or any other acronym standing for an examination, your goal for the test is simple, yet difficult, a perfect score.

While my Sunday mornings for those six months were spent in a classroom in the Student Union, it was because of those Sunday morning teaching sessions along with the numerous hours of studying and countless practice exams that I completed, that enabled me to score well on the exam.

The review course helps to essentially force you to study and review for the exam and does a great job teaching tricks to solving problems that are difficult and can occasionally take a long time to arrive at an answer.

Review courses also can help students whose problem is not their mastery of the material, but a problem with time management. The sections to complete on the exam are long. This often causes students to rush in order to complete all questions and thus score as high as possible.

Practicing and learning from an MCAT course instructor can help students learn ways to complete all the sections of the exam without fear of running out of time and having to guess on several problems or worse, leaving questions blank.

Review courses are rarely, if ever, free of charge and frequently cost anywhere from a few hundred to several thousand dollars depending on the type of teaching/tutoring you are looking for. With most students who graduate from medical school well over $100,000 in debt, the cost that accompanies a review course is miniscule in the long run and well worth it in the end.

11.   Medical School Commitment

"To be or not to be..." -- William Shakespeare.

While William Shakespeare was not a pre-medical student, his famous quote highlights the importance of having a commitment to a career in medicine prior to signing up and studying for the MCAT. Unlike some other graduate school admission examinations, the MCAT is not something that a student just decides to sign up and take on a whims notice.

Studying for the MCAT is a marathon, not a sprint. Depending on the person you ask and what sources you review, many would agree that six to nine months is a sufficient amount of time to study, review, and master material needed to perform well on the MCAT. You will encounter many variations on how long it takes to study for the MCAT, with some ranging from just a few weeks to over a year. In the opinion of myself and many of my colleagues, you should be finished with or finishing all courses which will be tested on the MCAT prior to actually taking the examination. It is very difficult to study for the medical school admissions examination without having sufficient knowledge of the subjects that you will be tested.

Plan on having your general physics, general chemistry, biology courses, and at least one semester of organic chemistry finished at least three months prior to taking the examination. Following the year 2015, with the addition of a section titled Psychological, Social, and Biological Foundations of Behavior, introductory courses in psychology and sociology should also be complete prior to sitting for the MCAT examination. This should allow sufficient time to have reviewed material that was completed many months or years earlier as well as the most recent courses.

12. Letters of Recommendation

It is often frustrating trying to obtain letters of recommendation for use with your medical school application. Many students don't know which professors they should ask for a letter of recommendation, partly because they don't have a relationship with their professors outside of being a face in the auditorium. It can be difficult to have a professional relationship with a professor of a core science course. This is especially true when you attend a university that has several hundred students per course per semester. When you are doing well in a course, you will often avoid a professor's office hours because attending office hours are usually not an efficient use of your time.

Letters of recommendation are an important part of your application; they help to give the admission board members an idea of the type of student you are from the perspective of another member of academia. Before asking for a letter of recommendation, you should go through a checklist in your head:

✓ Does that professor know you as more than a student ID number and letter grade?

✓ Are you going to earn an A in the course?

✓ Have you introduced yourself to the professor earlier in the semester and followed up with visits to the office during the professor's office hours at least every other week during the semester?

Identify which professor you would like to receive a letter from and ask them around midway through the semester, in person, if they are willing and able to write you a strong letter of recommendation for medical school. Asking early in the semester rather than after the course has finished will help to set an image in the professor's mind that you are goal-oriented and are not expecting a favor from them at the last-minute.

Ask the letter writer what information they would like to have to help make your letter as strong and personal as possible. Even if they do not ask for any additional information, provide your letter writer with a copy of your resume with passport sized professional photo in the corner and a copy of your personal statement. This will help them to write the strongest letter possible on your behalf.

Make sure to follow up their agreement for writing the letter with a thank you note or email the following day. This also helps to serve as a standing reminder on their desk on in their email box about drafting your letter of recommendation.

It is also important to ask the letter writer for a timetable that they would like in order to complete the letter. You should plan on at least three to four weeks in order for the letter to be completed. In the final week in which they agreed to complete the letter, send a reminder email with the instructions on how and to whom they need to send the completed letter.

Once the letter has been received and uploaded by your school's letter writing service (which is shown on your medical school application status), send a hand-written thank you card to your letter writer. Beyond the professional courtesy and good manners involved with sending a hand written thank-you note, your good manners will also help to pay it forward for students in the years behind you who will need letters of recommendation. Professors do not want to take the time to write dozens of letters of recommendation every year if it is thankless.

13. Personal Statement

The personal statement is probably the area of a medical student's application that needs the most work. Admittedly, I fell into this category when I applied to medical school. The standard medical school personal statement typically starts with a story of how the student has been interested in medicine since they were a little kid or how they always were fascinated with science and the inner workings of the human body. While these are invariably true statements for the vast majority of medical students, it is a story that is read repetitively by members of the medical school admissions committee.

Occasionally, a truly great personal statement is written by a student telling a heartwarming story of how they or a loved one overcame great struggle or illness, in a way that comes across on paper as if it was made for the silver screen.

Do not fret, a large number of medical students have not had an awe-inspiring life changing struggle, but still manage to write an excellent personal statement.

Your personal statement should capture the reader within the first paragraph, the first or second sentence for that matter. If it is boring for you to write and proof read, imagine what an admissions committee member reading hundreds of personal statements will feel like.

Use the personal statement as a way to highlight the events and activities you have been a part of throughout your life which have shaped you into the individual that you are. Think about an event or series of events that you aided in or witnessed, tying in the lessons you learned. How will you utilize those ideals in your everyday life as a medical student and future physician?

Additionally, make sure to write a personal statement that details why you would make an excellent and contributing member in the college of medicine. The personal statement is the only time that you can tell an admissions committee about yourself in your own words. This should provide details and tell a story one would not gather by just looking at your transcripts, test scores, and extracurricular activities.

The goal for your personal statement should be to "jump off the page" to the reader. They should finish reading your statement and want to talk more with you because they believe that you would be a tremendous addition to their medical school.

It is difficult to give examples of personal statements which are universally viewed as excellent. This is due to the fact that every person has different opinions on what they want to see in a personal statement.

Examples of bad sentences and paragraphs within a personal statement are easier to identify and address:

> *...I have always been interested in a career in medicine and as a doctor. Ever since I was in 5th grade, I would always raise my hand to answer questions during science class. I was always curious about the human body and how the functions of the body were changed during diseases and illnesses...*

...I think that I would be a good choice for (insert medical school name here) because I work hard and am a team player. As an honest and dependent student, I would also be able to help my fellow classmates in the event someone was not understanding the material and needed to join in my study group...

What did you think while reading that excerpt of a personal statement? Did this essay stand out? Did the student "jump off the page"?

I know that you all have an interest in the human body and how it functions (aka: anatomy and physiology), it is obvious that you do, or at least should have this interest; why else would you be applying to medical school?

The personal statement excerpt above also demonstrates a feeble attempt to discuss the writer's strengths. Working hard and being a team player are phenomenal qualities to have, but your personal statement should explain how working hard and being a team player have together brought you to where you are now.

Also, I would advise students to avoid the sentences like the last one in the second paragraph of the previous example statement entirely. Honesty, while probably the most important quality a physician should have, should describe *every* student applying to medical school.

Personal statements are always about quality, not quantity, and often ¾ to one page is enough to engage the admissions committee, telling them about yourself and why you would make a successful addition to their medical school. There are occasions where a longer personal statement is acceptable, but be wary of the fact that unless you are telling a story that is captivating to the reader, there are some medical school admission committee members who will simply stop reading a long personal statement after one page.

14. Extracurricular Activities/Leadership/Volunteering

There are very few students who are invited for medical interviews and even fewer students who are granted admission to medical school who do not have a résumé that boasts a number of extracurricular activities, leadership roles, and volunteer hours. Your extracurricular activities should also help tell medical school admission boards a little more about yourself prior to them reading your personal statement and inviting you for an interview. While it is nice to be a member of many different student associations on campus, it looks even better if you have held a leadership role within that organization. This helps medical school admission committees realize that along with a busy college course schedule you are able to also handle the responsibilities that go along with being a leader in a student run organization.

There are a number of student run organizations in medical school. There is everything from medical specialty interest groups, such as cardiology, surgery, or pediatrics, to groups focused more on organized medicine and the future of the medical profession as a whole, like the American Medical Association (AMA).

Many of the faculty, with whom you will be interviewing, serve as advisors to student-run interest groups. They often like to recommend students for admission who they think will not only perform well in the classroom, but will also help to give back to the school and medical profession as a whole through their involvement with medical school student run organizations.

High school and college are chock-full of free time, regardless of your major and course load. It is important to spend free time doing things you love, but also important to volunteer your time helping an organization.

Volunteer hours are not something that you get paid for, so your summer job tutoring freshman in calculus or working as a lifeguard does not count as volunteer work, but does count as work experience on your résumé.

While applications for medical school will not make volunteer work a requirement, I doubt there have been many medical students in the last 10 years who did not have a single volunteer hour on their medical school resume.

> *Fact or Fiction: All volunteer hours need to be done at a hospital or in a patient care setting if you want to get into medical school.*
>
> *Fiction: While it is always nice to have patient care experience while you are in college, it is about time spent volunteering with any charity or cause that is important.*

Many medical schools would prefer their students to have some clinical exposure prior to acceptance into medical school. After all, how do you know you if a career as a physician is for you if you have had zero exposure to it prior to medical school?

- ✓ Consider shadowing a physician who works at a hospital or clinic on your or near your college campus.
- ✓ Ask to shadow your pediatrician or family physician during summer or breaks from school.
- ✓ Volunteer at a local hospital or clinic. Most hospitals have formal programs for volunteers which can be found by searching the hospital's website for their volunteer coordinator.

15. Research

This section of the application is most often blank. To be involved in research during your time as an undergraduate student is difficult because of the time commitment that is often involved. With a little planning, this can be accomplished and will serve as an instant boost to any medical school application. Most colleges and universities keep a list of research projects their faculty members are currently involved in on the school's website.

Additionally, because many professors and clinicians associated with a university are research-oriented, be confident in asking your professors about what projects they are currently involved in, and if there are any opportunities for you to assist with the research. Even if they are not involved in any research projects at the time, they will probably know of a colleague that has a research project that could use an extra mind and set of hands.

I was enrolled for six credits during the summer session following my freshman year in college. With my course load light during the summer semester, I was able to take time to find and work on a research project.

My goal entering college was always to attend medical school and eventually become a pediatric plastic surgeon. With that idea in mind, I set out to shadow and hopefully perform research with a plastic surgeon at the University of Florida College of Medicine. I started by locating the names and email addresses of each of the surgeons at the college of medicine and drafted an email which detailed who I was and what I was hoping to accomplish during my next three years at the University of Florida. Of the several emails that I sent, I was fortunate to have one physician respond stating that he would allow me to shadow him in the operating room on a weekly basis. He also told me of research project idea that he would like to begin if I was interested.

I don't think that I could have responded fast enough to the email, which by the way is a reminder for me to tell you to always use spell check. It is very unprofessional to send emails which contain gross spelling and grammar mistakes.

E-mail is acceptable and in many cases, the preferred method of communication during college and medical school. When addressing an email to a professor or physician, there are a few things to remember so that your email comes across as professional, giving you the best chance to have your question or request answered/granted.

Contrary to what you may have been taught, you do not need to address your emails with "Dear _____". Additionally, you should introduce yourself at the beginning of the email and quickly get into your question or request. Long emails, especially the first email to a professor or physician who is not expecting it are often skimmed over and may not yield the results you expect. A basic email to a professor or physician coming from a student can be organized the following way:

Dr. Rudnick,

I am a freshman, majoring in _____ at the University of _____ with an interest in a career as a physician with a potential research focus. I came across your research project (titled....) via the college of medicine website and would like to know if there are any opportunities for a freshman student on your research team. I am able to serve in any capacity you deem necessary on the research project.

I am able to provide a copy of my CV for your review and meet in person to discuss any opportunities you may have. In the event you do not have a position available on your research team, are you aware of any colleagues who may have a position for an undergraduate researcher?

Thank you for your time. I look forward to hearing from you soon.

Sincerely,

Name
Contact info

During that summer, I began a research project where I compiled all of the data and background information as well as writing the first draft of a manuscript titled "Access to Hand Surgery Emergency Care" that would later be accepted for publication in the *Annals of Plastic Surgery*. While my medical career choice, general pediatrics, went in a direction very different from plastic surgery, the experience of being involved with a scientific research project and going through the manuscript submission process is invaluable to my future as a physician.

I will tell you now that it can be difficult for an undergraduate student to be involved in research that will lead to a published manuscript. However, publication is something that you should aspire to if you are to become involved in a research project during your undergraduate career.

Learning about the process by which an idea is turned into a research project design, Institutional Review Board (IRB) approval, data gathering, manuscript drafts, and finally, the publication review process, was important for my career as a physician. It is also a great discussion topic while being interviewed for medical school, especially when the interviewer is also involved in research. Publishing a peer-reviewed scientific paper is an accomplishment that will stay with you for your entire career, as well as a testament to your abilities to design and carry out a beneficial research idea.

V. Interviewing For Medical School

The interview for medical school can be a huge boost to your application. There are several thousand applications to most medical schools every year. Out of the thousands of applications reviewed by members of the admissions committee, maybe a few hundred students will be invited for an interview.

Making it this far in the application process is great, but it means nothing if you are not able to impress your interviewers to help your candidacy for that particular program.

16. Knowledge

The first key to a successful interview is knowledge. This does not mean that you need to know the management for acute appendicitis, but rather knowledge about your own application. There have been several instances where I have heard of interviewers asking about items which were listed in a student's application, only to have the student stumble over an answer as to what the volunteer work or extracurricular activity was about. You should know your application inside and out, which is part of the reason why you should always document a few sentences about the experiences you had as an undergraduate student which are listed on your medical school application.

✓ Tip: keep a document (separate from your résumé) where you write 2 or 3 sentences about what you did during each volunteer or extracurricular activity and what you may have learned from it.

✓ Review this prior to every interview so that you do not hesitate if asked about a particular part of your application.

While some schools will have "closed application" interviews, meaning that the interviewer will not have access to your application file prior to your interview, it is still imperative to be able to speak about the experiences you listed on your application in case you are asked during the interview.

Additionally, a successful interviewee must have knowledge about the school to which they are applying. You probably won't need to know who founded the university or college to which you are applying, but you will need to have an understanding of the type of hospital facilities which you will be rotating. Applicants should be aware of the medical school's main hospital and trauma center status, (i.e. level one, two, etc.) and the type of curriculum upon which the school bases its course design. Knowing this information will help you appear to the interviewer that you do actually want to attend their medical school and will help you to pre-formulate a few questions that you can ask during your interview.

All interviewers will ask if you have any questions for them at some point during the interview. Sometimes, they lead with that question and basically allow you to dictate how the interview will flow. Have several questions prepared in advance, in your head, not read off of your notes about the school. This will also help the conversation flow seamlessly. Along with having a question in mind, be prepared to explain why you are asking the question.

For instance, having completed and published a clinical research paper during my undergraduate years, I always asked about opportunities and ease of becoming involved with research early in my medical school career. At the time of asking my question, I would lead with something to the effect of,

"I was involved in a research project during my undergraduate years and had the opportunity to co-author a manuscript which was published in the *Annals of Plastic Surgery*, what research opportunities and avenues are in place for first year medical students?"

This allows you to not only ask your question, but also provides insight to the interviewer about why you are asking the question. It also gives them information about yourself that they may not be aware of, especially if you are at a medical school which uses closed application interviews. Examples of other questions:

- ✓ "I had the privilege of volunteering at a free clinic for underserved families while in college. What opportunities are there in place for medical students to become involved with providing care to the underserved population in this city?"
- ✓ "I have an interest in attending an international medical mission trip, are there any faculty members who organize international mission trips with the medical students?"
- ✓ "Are lectures recorded and put online so that material can be reviewed after a particular lecture?"

17. Confidence

Regardless of how outgoing or shy you may be, it is important to come across as confident, but not arrogant, to the interviewer. Medical schools very rarely want to offer acceptance to an overly confident and arrogant-appearing student who believes that they already have the knowledge necessary to be a cardiovascular surgeon. At the same time, speaking confidently about the topics or questions you are asked about helps to show that you are likely able to carry on an intelligent conversation with a professor or attending physician. It also shows you will likely speak respectfully and to the educational level and understanding of your patients.

Patients often are more likely to adhere to a medication or treatment regimen if they believe that the physician feels strongly in its effectiveness. A simple change in inflection or tone of voice can help patients feel that their treatment plan will work, and with the placebo-effect well documented, a portion of patients will feel better even if their treatment plan was not perfect.

Confidence is not just about how you speak during your interview, but also about body language. There should be a balance between sitting like a statue and squirming around in your chair like a seven year old who wants to go to recess. If you frequently use your hands while you speak, it is ok to continue, so long as you do not draw attention away from what you are saying. Small and fluid, not spastic, hand movements can help accentuate the points you are making during your interview and can make your responses more memorable to the interviewer.

Whether sitting with both feet on the floor, or choosing to cross your legs, gentlemen and ladies, are all acceptable so long as you do not appear like you are lounging at home on your couch. There are some students who have a tendency during an interview, especially when they are nervous, to sway their upper body slowly back and forth while answering a question. This habit is extremely distracting to an interviewer and can actually cause them to think about whether or not you are a pendulum, rather than listen to your eloquent response.

Other keys to a successful interview:

- ✓ Eye contact should be kept at all times while speaking and being spoken to. Eye contact does not mean that you can't blink!
- ✓ Remember to smile (appropriately and intermittently) when you are introducing yourself and while listening to the interviewer speak. This subtle cue helps to assure the interviewer that you are paying attention to what they are saying.
- ✓ A firm handshake should always be extended to the interviewer prior to and after your meeting. This holds true for both men and women.

18. Dress to Impress

Dress to impress, a great adage to remember for your medical school interview and every interview for the rest of your life. I have seen hundreds of candidates for medical school and residency while on their tours of my campus or hospital. And, forgive me gentlemen, but there have been applicants, mostly men, who are dressed like they took a suit from their much taller and rotund father and put it on for the interview.

A well fitting suit for both men and women can help you stand out just a little more than another applicant. A suit jacket that fits well, along with a shirt and tie, or blouse that matches can help give your interview a slight boost. Since many of us will not fit perfectly into a suit jacket or pants which are off the rack at a department store, take the initiative to have the jacket and pants tailored to fit your body type. This involves using the tailor located at the store where you bought the suit or bringing it to a professional who performs clothing alterations in your community so that the suit fits you and not the mannequin.

Candidates often ask if it is ok to wear bright colors on their interview day, rather than the standard black suit, white shirt/blouse, and blue tie. Putting color into your interview wardrobe is a great way to stand out a little more, but remember to do so within reason.

I have always been a believer that if you look good, you feel good, which will help your confidence during your interviews.

Your interview outfit may be set, but in addition to your well fitted suit, don't forgot to come well rested and well groomed to the interview.

- ✓ Clean shaven or groomed facial hair.
- ✓ Haircut and professional style – meaning that it's probably not a good idea to show up with a purple mohawk. That may be your style, but remember, interviewers, whether you agree with it or not, tend to want to accept students who are like themselves.
- ✓ Avoid the out-of-bed look.
- ✓ Keep accessories and jewelry simple and professional. If it clangs and clacks every time you move, it might be best to leave it in your suitcase.

Entering into the field of medicine is a commitment of your time and money. Medical school is not cheap and the cost of at least one nice interview outfit pales in comparison, so start saving a little money now and invest in an outfit that is yours and makes you feel proud and confident.

VI. Where Should I Go to Medical School?

I was told during my freshman year of college that if you only get into one medical school, go there. When it comes to choosing a school from a list of acceptances or just choosing which schools to apply, the decision is more challenging.

Medical schools can be divided into 2 main categories, M.D. (Medical Doctor) and D.O. (Doctor of Osteopathic Medicine). The M.D. category can be further divided into M.D. programs which are located in the United States and those which are located in the Caribbean. All categories involve similar education; all are four years of teaching, which are then followed by residency of three to seven years, depending on your specialty.

Caribbean schools, while usually less expensive and slightly easier to be accepted to than traditional M.D. programs, are not all created equal. There are some programs which are not accredited in the United States, meaning that graduates from those programs will not be able to begin their residency program in the United States once finished with medical school. There are a few very good programs located throughout the Caribbean; however, the general consensus is that their graduates typically have a much more difficult time earning a spot in a top-tier United States residency program.

Additionally, many Caribbean programs have their students complete their third and fourth years in the United States, usually New York or Florida. Because the hospitals which their students complete clinical rotations in vary greatly, even within the same school, learning can be sporadic and not as organized as most programs located in the United States.

When I asked current resident physicians and rotating medical students why they chose attend an international/Caribbean based medical school, several stated that they were not accepted to an M.D. or D.O. program located in the United States.

Others stated that they chose the Caribbean based M.D. program over a Doctor of Osteopathic Medicine (D.O.) program because of the potential stigma and naivety of people who do not know what type of physician and training a student graduating with a D.O. actually has. For a lot of them, it was truly about the letters behind their name.

Doctor of Osteopathic Medicine, D.O., has education similar to traditional M.D. programs. They have added curriculum of osteopathic manipulation, which focuses on the musculoskeletal system and how it correlates with disease and disability.

D.O. medical students can apply for most residency programs, provided they take the same licensing exam as M.D. students, known as the USMLE (United States Medical Licensing Exam), rather than the licensing exam known as the COMLEX (Comprehensive Osteopathic Medical Licensing Examination). There is a disadvantage with taking only the D.O. licensing exam in that you cannot apply for a M.D. residency program without also taking the USMLE.

Medical students who graduate from D.O. programs can still earn a position in a top-tier residency program, however, some physicians believe that it is a slight disadvantage when applying to programs compared to M.D. students with similar scores and resumes. Additionally, some residency programs simply will not interview or accept students who graduate with a D.O. degree.

The most common of the three types of medical schools are M.D. programs located in the United States. There are 136 as of the year 2012, with most fairly similar in their curriculum. Programs are ranked and rated based on a variety of factors which can all be found online. All of the United States M.D. programs graduate their students as a medical doctor (M.D.), there are slight differences in their curriculum. Some schools have ever changing curriculum which teaches medicine along with cutting edge technologies which are poised to change the way that physicians treat patients and practice medicine.

Students often have a difficult time choosing which schools to send their application. One very important factor is to choose a school in a location which you will be comfortable living for the next four years. Medical school is extremely arduous and at times seemingly insurmountable. When you are in a city that you are comfortable and have friends or family nearby, it helps to get you through the most trying times during your medical school career. Students interested in a medical career with a research focus may want to apply and choose to attend a medical school that has higher percentage of successful research oriented faculty.

Many pre-med college students make the mistake of applying only to a small number of medical schools or applying to only nationally acclaimed programs. Whether this is done because they are overconfident or because they were told by professors and advisors that they were a "lock" to get into the school or schools of their choice, it is not a good strategy to have. Students should utilize the resources available to them online through the Association of American Medical Colleges (www.aamc.org). Here, data on the average GPA and MCAT score can be viewed over the past several years.

Knowing where you stand as an applicant based first on your MCAT score and GPA will help you understand which medical school programs fall in three major categories, which are different for every student.

- ✓ Reach schools – those which have higher average scores in MCAT and GPA compared to your scores
- ✓ In your ballpark – schools with average MCAT scores and GPA which are at or very near your scores
- ✓ Safety schools – schools with lower average MCAT (by at least 4.0 points) and GPA compared to your scores

Students should apply to programs in all three categories listed above with the majority of their applications going to schools that are "in your ballpark" and safety schools, and less applications going to schools which may be a greater reach.

There may be a slight bias in the general community determined by the name of your medical school as it relates to the perceived "prestige" and tradition. The truth is that nearly any student with great medical board examination scores, graduating near the top of their medical school class, and with a number of research publications, are likely be accepted into a residency in the medical specialty field of their choice.

VII. Life Outside of Medical School

Between the marathon study sessions and late night pizza ordering, there still is time for life outside of medical school. Surprisingly, one of the hardest adjustments for medical students is explaining to their family and close friends the massive amounts of material presented to them each day during lectures. Parents and friends often don't understand why, if you were able to have time to visit with them as an undergraduate, it differs once accepted into medical school.

The balance of life in and outside of medical school must be achieved in order for you to achieve your goals while still taking time to do the things you love.

19. A Balancing Act

An article I wrote in 2010 about the balance in a medical student's life.

A Balancing Act
The Other Side of a Medical Student's Life

With the turn of the calendar to April, countless things begin to change. Spring begins to come into full bloom (meaning allergy problems for millions), medical students start thinking about the end of the year (and the excitement and terror of matriculating to the next level), and most importantly, baseball season begins. Few things to me are as exciting to me as the first pitch of baseball season; whether I am in the stands eating a hot dog staring wide eyed as my team takes the field, or home enjoying the game on the couch with franks in a blanket, the feeling that still comes over me at the beginning of each season is unlike any other.

While watching Marlins shortstop Hanley Ramirez step up to the plate, stay back and hit an off speed pitch to right field, I can't help but think about the enormous amount of balance required. Now for those of you who do not follow baseball obsessively like myself, you may not realize that hitting a baseball is about more than strength and bat speed. I recently had a realization that medicine and baseball are not entirely dissimilar. While they both require vigorous training, skill, and time, the most important commonality is ability to understand balance.

While in medical school, I learned quickly that in order to truly succeed, one needs to utilize balance, a learning objective that we acquire at a very young age on the playground. All those days during recess where my classmates and I would learn how many kids it would take to make the balance beam be completely still, neutral, even though forces were trying to tip it to one side.

Medical school is no different. It takes balance to succeed during those first 4 years. With the intense weight and pressure that the demands of a medical education bring, I needed to equal, or in most cases attempt to equal out those demands with people and events in my life. But it is not easy trying to balance the other side of a beam with the weight of what seems to be the product of three sumo wrestlers. While the avenues chosen in order to bring about the balance are likely different for every person, for me they included sports, spending time with friends, and enjoying time off with my wife (girlfriend and fiancée at the time). Playing intramural sports at USF and watching nearly any sport on TV that included my favorite teams (I'm a south Florida homer: Marlins, Heat, and Dolphins) helped to create some weight on the other side of my balance beam of life, essentially equaling one of the three sumo wrestlers.

Friends, be they medical students or otherwise, are extremely important in order to bring my balance beam toward neutral. There are no other people who can truly understand the trials and tribulations of being a medical student besides other medical students and every one of us needs to vent at times. Whether about a poor test score or an attending that is pimping us to no end, it is these friends that are there to listen and offer advice on what items to focus on for examinations or what resources to use in order to shine during hour long pimp sessions with attendings; another sumo wrestler balanced.

Just like when a baseball takes a tricky hop and turns a routine groundout into a base hit for a batter, I was as lucky to be introduced to my wife. While that is a long story that is not for this article, my wife provides me with the final piece in order to balance my medical life and personal life. She helps me keep a level head on my shoulders and always helps to bring an outsider perspective to the struggles of medical school.

Whether we are each on our computers working, or enjoying an evening out on the town (as rare as they are in medical school) I always know that at the end of the day, excluding nights on call, we will be together. I had no idea that the final piece to my balance beam would be so beautiful and funny, but I am lucky. (Just like the Marlins in game 6 of the 2003 NLCS, remember Steve Bartman?)

After taking the time to reflect on what it takes to balance medical life with personal life, I realize that balance during residency and beyond can be achieved. I have seen firsthand with my preceptors and mentors, that those with balance between personal life and medical obligations speak the most about their happiness.

While my career as a professional baseball player may never come to fruition, my vigorous training, skill, and balance may just prepare me to handle anything off-speed.

VIII. What Kind of Doctor Should I Be?

Take solace in the fact that the majority of incoming medical students usually do not know what kind of doctor they want to be. A portion of those, myself included, who thought they had an idea of what kind of physician they would like to become at the start of medical school, did not end up in that field.

I was once told, with regard to what specialty of medicine to pursue, that you should practice whatever area of medicine you love to read about. Learning as a physician is never ending and the moment you stop, you conclude your time as a growing doctor. This is something that should never happen as long as you are treating patients.

As a resident physician, my colleagues and I occasionally remark at the treatment choices recommended to patients by some community doctors. These patients may receive tests and treatments which are not evidence based or based on protocols and algorithms that are outdated and have been revised several times over the years.

Reviewing these treatment plans helps to illustrate the point to young physicians that once you fall out of academic medicine and fail to keep up with new and emerging treatments and evidence-based algorithms, you may start to fail your patients.

We owe it to our patients and to the practice of medicine to be as well informed as possible and to be flexible in thoughts and treatment plans. I remember being told in my first week of medical school that medicine changes every 5 years, and half of what we learn while in medical school will someday be proven incorrect. The only problem is we don't know which half.

There are more than 120 different medical specialties for medical students to choose from for their career as a physician. As a medical student, you will have the opportunity to learn about and hopefully be exposed to most, if not all of the medical specialties. Medical students are exposed to the different areas of medicine either as a requirement for graduation from or as an elective rotation during the third and fourth years of medical school.

Following the fourth year of medical school, newly graduated students, now physicians, enter their residency training where they complete typically between three to seven years of training prior to being able to practice medicine on their own. Additionally, once residency has been completed, physicians have the option to apply for a fellowship in a medical subspecialty such as, cardiology, pulmonology, allergy & immunology, as well as many others for anywhere from one to five or more years, depending on the specialty.

A list of potential residency choices for medical students and the number of years ( ) to complete them are listed:

Family Medicine (3)

Internal Medicine (3)

Pediatrics (3)

Emergency Medicine (3)

Obstetrics & Gynecology (4)

Pathology (3-4)

Anesthesiology (4)

Dermatology (4)

Neurology (4)

Ophthalmology (4)

Psychiatry (4)

Radiology (5)

Orthopedic Surgery (5)

Otolaryngology (ENT) (5)

Urology (5)

General Surgery (5)

Plastic Surgery (5-7)

Surgical Subspecialties (5-8)

IX. Social Media Profiles

Recent data from Facebook stated that there were over 14 million users aged 13-17 on their site. With the numbers in the teenage bracket expected to continuously climb, it is likely that the majority of college and medical school applicants will have an online profile on any number of social media websites.

Students must take full responsibility for everything that is posted on their profile, whether or not they wrote it. It should be assumed that regardless of privacy settings, anything a student writes, or any pictures which they are in, have the potential to be viewed by the college and medical school admission committee when their applications are reviewed.

Colleges and medical schools want to accept students who will represent the morals and traditions which the university or college was founded on, not someone who is constantly posting racist or sexist comments or engaging in inappropriate or illegal acts in pictures on their or someone else's profile.

A rule of thumb that I tell all of my adolescent-aged patients is that anything they post online should be acceptable not only to them, but also their mother, grandmother, and school principal. Take responsibility now, create strict privacy settings, and assume that anything you comment on, post, or what is posted about you online will be accessible to the admissions board members of the school you wish to attend.

I have seen an increasing trend over the past few years by students who change their name on Facebook, Twitter, or other social media profile pages to avoid college and medical school admission committee members from viewing their profile, comments, and pictures. This is a practice that is very prevalent, especially amongst fourth year medical students during the residency application season. There may be programs, colleges, and medical schools, that attempt to view potential candidates' social media profiles in an attempt to learn more about them and determine if they are someone who is a proper fit for their institution.

Should I change my social media profile name so that I am not identifiable or "searchable" by admission committees?

My suggestion to students is to use social media responsibly and expect that everything you post and in all pictures you appear can and will be viewed by an admissions board whether your name is on the profile or not.

There is no denying the future of medicine will in part utilize social media to enhance the patient-physician relationship and increase the quality of care that is provided. There are endless ways in which social media can enhance patient care. One of which can include a doctor keeping a professional Facebook page or blog site where they post articles about relevant health information and tips, or gives his or her opinion on a recent medical news story.

In my opinion, this type of communication helps patients feel that they are closer to their physician even though they may be reading it from a half a world away.

Pre-med and medical students along with residents and current physicians need to realize that social media in medicine is something that is here to stay. All students should start setting themselves up to utilize social media correctly and responsibly. First, by learning and utilizing security features available on social media profiles. This will help you to better serve your patients and improve the quality of your care.

X. Paying the Price

Data from the Association of American Medical Colleges from 2011 states that 87% of medical students from the class of 2011 graduated with some amount of educational debt. 77% of medical school graduates from 2011, myself included, graduated with over $100,000 in education debt, the majority of which is from the rising costs of medical school tuition and fees in the United States.

The commitment of your time (medical school is a full-time job) and money to become a physician is undeniable. While there are a few students whose families are able to supplement their medical education either full or in part, take solace in the fact that nearly all of your medical school classmates and attending physicians will have medical school debt that they are in the process of acquiring or paying off once they finish medical school.

The question that almost always comes up when I speak with high school students is how they will be able to afford the cost of medical school. There are a number of medical student loan services, both public and private which will provide you money (which you must repay) to pay for your medical school tuition, fees, and cost of living. Interest rates, while relatively low, are charged on the loans meaning that you will have to pay back much more than you originally had to borrow while in medical school.

The good news is that once your loans begin to require repayment, which is almost always not until after medical school is completed, you are usually able to repay a small amount per month while in residency when your salary is only a fraction of what it will be once you are a practicing physician. After residency, when monthly payments rise, so should your salary, making repayment a nuisance, but still possible.

Most, if not all, medical schools in the United States will have a dedicated staff member who will aid students with acquiring loans before medical school begins as well as helping to set up repayments once your medical school career has finished.

XI. If I Become A Doctor, Will I Be A Millionaire?

While many people may be under the impression that doctors make an exorbitant amount of money, the fact is nearly all physicians do not make millions, but rest assure, can live a very comfortable lifestyle. I am sorry to break the bad news to those of you who believe that all doctors are millionaires and have vacation homes in the mountains or on the beach.

As I have been told by physicians in practice for more than 20 years, there was once a "golden age" for physician reimbursement. A time where physicians were paid extremely well for the care and procedures they performed.

Our healthcare system is constantly looking for ways to save money, and private and public insurance companies are attempting to pay doctors less and less each year.

Despite what rumors you have heard about doctors being poor and frequently unable to make ends meet, physicians still make a comfortable salary. The purpose of a career in medicine is a burning desire to help people in a time of sickness; to educate and treat someone on the prevention and control of disease and disability.

You must devote yourself to a career which is constantly evolving and to a career where half of what you learned in medical school may be proven false within 5 to 10 years. Every day when I read articles and research abstracts, I am constantly reminded how much about medicine I have not yet learned and how much of what I thought I knew has changed. It is this perpetual change that drives me to never stop learning so that I can be the best pediatrician for my patients and provide them with the most evidence-based care that they deserve.

So really, how much money do doctors make?

The average physician salary varies greatly, with specialists almost always having a higher salary than general practitioners (i.e. pediatricians, internists, and family medicine physicians). A survey of more than 15,000 physicians from Medscape's 2011 Compensation Survey found that the top salaries on average were in the fields of orthopedic surgery, radiology, cardiology, and anesthesiology.

The medical fields at the lower end of the average physician salary scale were endocrinology, primary care, and pediatrics. The lower end of the average physician pay scale was around $150,000 per year and the highest paid specialties, orthopedic surgery and radiology around $350,000 per year.

Physician salaries with the averages as listed above can be significantly higher, with many earning well over $500,000 per year. This largely depends on which specialty or field of medicine you enter, whether you work for a hospital or physician group, whether you agree to be paid based on a yearly salary or based on your performance/income generated, and how many hours/days you want to work per week.

Additionally, there are many physicians who make a much lower yearly salary than the average. Some have a lower salary because they would rather have more time for medical research projects or a lifestyle where they work part-time.

Remember, most physicians still earn a salary that is well above average. While the average salaries may seem like a lot or a little depending on who is reading this, know that most physicians work much more than an average 40 hour work week.

There are many ways to become a millionaire, but it is highly unlikely that today's practice of medicine is one of them. If you are interested in making a quick million, put this book down and get to work on your internet company. However, for those ready to accept the challenges and responsibilities of caring for people's lives whether you make a $1,000,000 or not, you have finished this book and on your way to becoming a doctor.

In good health and good luck
Dr. Chad Rudnick, MD

Timeline

Grade 9

☐ Study and complete all homework assignments on time.

☐ Study hard, earn A's, and earn college credit by passing all of your advanced placement end-of-the-year examinations.

☐ Ask for extra help as soon as you believe that you are struggling with a class or anytime you earn a C or lower on an exam.

☐ Begin or continue volunteering in your community.

☐ Become involved in extracurricular activities or athletics at your school or within your community.

☐ Begin to create your résumé with the basic information listed in Chapter 3, Section 7.

Grade 10

- ☐ Study and complete all homework assignments on time.
- ☐ Study hard, earn A's, and earn college credit by passing all of your advanced placement end-of-the-year examinations.
- ☐ Ask for extra help as soon as you believe that you are struggling with a class or anytime you earn a C or lower on an exam.
- ☐ Continue your volunteer involvement in your community.
- ☐ Add all honors, awards, extracurricular activities, leadership roles, volunteer work, and work experience to your résumé.
- ☐ Near the end of your sophomore year, begin to determine which SAT or ACT preparation courses or materials you will use.

Grade 11

- ☐ Study and complete all homework assignments on time.
- ☐ Study hard, earn A's, and earn college credit by passing all of your advanced placement end-of-the-year examinations.

- ☐ Ask for extra help as soon as you believe that you are struggling with a class or anytime you earn a C or lower on an exam.
- ☐ Continue your volunteer involvement in your community.
- ☐ Add all honors, awards, extracurricular activities, volunteer work, and work experience to your résumé.
- ☐ Complete your college entrance exams (standardized tests) early in your junior year so that another attempt can be completed in the event you do not score as high as you expected.
- ☐ Begin to search online and with your high school guidance counselor for colleges and universities that you would like to attend. Determine each school's requirements and average admission scores and GPA to determine your potential strength for admission.
- ☐ Determine if the college or university has a pre-med program for students interested in medical school.
- ☐ Has the college or university had a large number of students accepted into medical school directly from college?

- [ ] Visit as many of the colleges or universities which you are considering applying to as you can. Especially your top choices.
- [ ] Near the end of your junior year, begin to prepare materials that you will need in order to apply to the colleges and universities of your choice.
- [ ] Think about who you would like to write a letter of recommendation on your behalf for acceptance to college. Review chapter 4, section 12 for tips on obtaining strong letters of recommendation. Don't forget your thank-you notes! Handwritten!

Grade 12

- [ ] Do I still need to tell you to study, complete assignments, and ask for help when you need it?
- [ ] The summer prior to beginning your senior year of high school, start completing your college applications and writing the essays which are required by the college or university for admission.
- [ ] Continue to update your résumé.
- [ ] Complete your college applications.

- ☐ Submit your college applications as soon as possible. Do not delay submission unless absolutely necessary, this is especially important for colleges and universities which use a rolling admissions process.
- ☐ Continue your involvement in your community through extracurricular and volunteer activities.
- ☐ Remember to pack *The Ultimate Guidebook For Getting Into Medical School* in your bag prior to leaving for your freshman year of college.

College Freshman

- ☐ Choose a major that you are interested in, being sure that you can fit all of the medical school required courses in along with your major's required courses.
- ☐ Stay on top of all of your classes, asking for help and visiting your professor's office hours any time to you feel you are not grasping the material.
- ☐ Become involved in the pre-medical society at your school.
- ☐ Become involved in other extracurricular activities and find volunteer opportunities both in the medical field and outside of the medical field.

Run for a leadership position within one or a few of the organizations you are involved with following your freshman year.

- [ ] Continue to update your résumé.
- [ ] Your goal is a 4.0 GPA.

College Sophomore

- [ ] Ensure that you are on track with your required medical school courses and will have general chemistry, physics, biology, and one semester of organic chemistry completed prior to the spring semester of your junior year.
- [ ] In the summer following your freshman year, begin your search for a research project that you can assist with. (review chapter 4, section 15)
- [ ] Continue involvement with the pre-medical society along with other extracurricular activities.
- [ ] Continue or for the first time, attempt to obtain a leadership position within the organizations you are involved with on your campus.
- [ ] Continue volunteer activities.
- [ ] Contact your pediatrician, family physician, or a local physician at or near your college to spend time shadowing them in the clinic or hospital.

☐ Determine if any of your professors would serve as strong letter of recommendation writers (chapter 4, section 12).

College Junior

☐ Continue to excel in your college courses.

☐ Continue your leadership positions, extracurricular activities, volunteer experience, and physician shadowing.

☐ Continue your research project and determine if you will have enough data to submit and publish a research abstract or research paper.

☐ The summer prior to your junior year, begin to look into MCAT preparation materials and courses to determine which type of materials or course is best for you (chapter 4, sections 8-10).

☐ Begin studying for the MCAT.

☐ Take the MCAT in the spring semester of your junior year.

☐ Begin to evaluate different medical schools and determine which schools fit your scores (review chapter 6).

☐ Update résumé.

- ☐ Identify and ask for letters of recommendation (review chapter 4, section 12). Don't forget your handwritten thank-you notes!
- ☐ Begin to work on your personal statement so that it is available for the writers of your letters of recommendation.

College Senior

- ☐ Complete your list of medical schools to which you will apply.
- ☐ Finalize your résumé and personal statement.
- ☐ Submit all medical school application materials as soon as possible after applications for the year.
- ☐ Continue your research projects.
- ☐ As interviews for medical school are extended to you, schedule them and begin to prepare by reviewing chapter 5.
- ☐ Update all of the medical schools you have applied to by sending them your Fall semester grades and any new information about your research projects, awards, or accomplishments.

About the author

Dr. Chad Rudnick is a pediatric resident physician at Miami Children's Hospital in Miami, FL. A published author, clinical research investigator, public speaker, and debate moderator, he was born and raised in Boca Raton, FL.

Dr. Rudnick completed his undergraduate studies at the University of Florida and attended medical school at the University of South Florida.

He appeared as a state wide representative for Florida's medical students with the American Cancer Society's "Pass the Buck" campaign on tobacco tax legislation.

Chad resides in Miami, FL with his wife, Ashley, and their dog, Snuggie. He maintains a pediatric based blog at www.chadrudnick.blogspot.com and can be followed on Twitter @Peds_doc.

More information on Dr. Rudnick can be found on his website www.DrChadRudnick.com.

Notes

Notes

Made in the USA
Charleston, SC
20 November 2012